THE AMA... SPIDER-MAN™

COLORING AND ACTIVITY BOOK

MARVEL SPIDER-MAN® MERCHANDISING

COLUMBIA PICTURES
© 2012 COLUMBIA PICTURES INDUSTRIES, INC. ALL RIGHTS RESERVED.

BENDON®
Publishing International, Inc.   Ashland, OH 44805   www.bendonpub.com

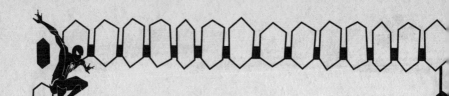

FOLLOW THE PATH

USING THE LETTERS, IN ORDER, FROM THE WORD **SECRET**,
FOLLOW THE CORRECT PATH TO FIND YOUR WAY THROUGH THE MAZE.

START

T	W	S	T	G	Y	Q	N
R	C	E	Q	T	S	E	Z
E	R	T	R	E	G	C	R
T	S	E	C	L	P	B	E
N	V	P	U	G	E	S	T
K	P	T	E	R	C	A	I
G	X	S	E	C	R	E	S
N	R	I	A	N	S	T	Q

FINISH

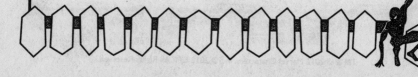

MATCHING

DRAW A LINE TO MATCH THE CHARACTERS TO THEIR SILHOUETTES.

IMAGE SCRAMBLE

* ADULT SUPERVISION REQUIRED!

CAREFULLY CUT OUT ALL OF THE PUZZLE PIECES IN THE BOTTOM GRID. GLUE OR TAPE THE PIECES TO THE SQUARE WITH THE MATCHING LETTER OR NUMBER ON THE TOP GRID.
*VARIATION: DRAW THE PIECES IN THE TOP GRID INSTEAD OF CUTTING AND PASTING THEM.

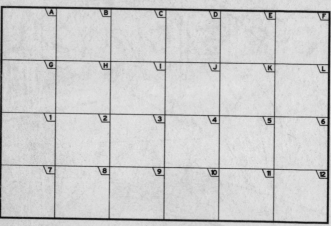

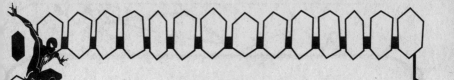

TRANSFER

**USING THE PATHS, TRANSFER THE LETTERS
INTO THE BOXES TO UNSCRAMBLE THE WORD.**

GRECAOU

ANSWER: COURAGE

WORD SEARCH

Find and circle the words in the puzzle below.

- BULLY
- HIGH SCHOOL
- QUIET
- CLASSES
- NOTEBOOK
- SMART

```
R  H  Z  F  D  S  P  P  R  M  Z  I  P
V  E  I  M  P  Z  S  Y  N  D  T  V  U
P  X  Q  G  R  R  W  J  C  K  C  K  C
U  A  M  T  H  B  V  D  U  Q  L  D  D
Y  K  L  M  Y  S  J  D  C  S  A  J  K
J  Z  H  L  A  W  C  T  C  H  S  Q  R
U  M  A  N  X  P  P  H  N  K  S  U  H
F  U  F  J  O  R  K  G  O  X  E  I  W
H  Q  F  C  R  I  U  O  O  O  S  E  U
W  B  D  D  U  H  B  C  B  G  L  T  S
S  G  U  Z  F  E  M  Z  U  G  U  I  M
F  D  P  Z  T  D  Y  A  L  Q  O  P  A
I  F  S  O  B  V  T  S  L  A  A  D  R
L  L  N  G  Q  N  V  B  Y  L  L  S  T
E  P  K  D  M  I  D  C  V  O  J  B  A
```

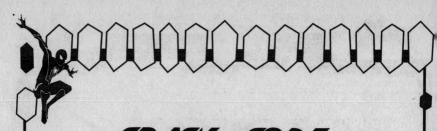

CRACK THE CODE
USING THE SECRET CODE BELOW, FILL IN THE BLANKS
AND REVEAL THE HIDDEN WORDS!

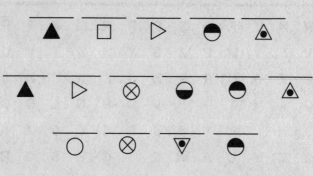

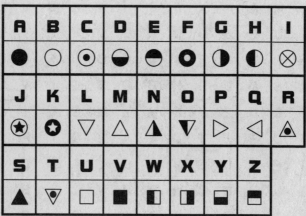

A	B	C	D	E	F	G	H	I
●	○	⊙	◑	◓	◕	◐	◑	⊗

J	K	L	M	N	O	P	Q	R
★	✪	▽	△	◭	▼	▷	◁	◬

S	T	U	V	W	X	Y	Z
▲	▼	□	■	◧	▨	▬	▬

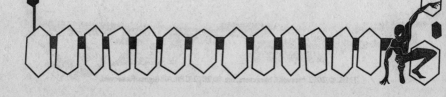

SECRET MESSAGE

Cross out the word **SPIDERMAN** every time you see it in the box. When you reach a letter that does not belong, write it in the shapes below to reveal the secret message.

SPIDERMANSPIDERMAN
SPIDERMANASPIDERMAN
GSPIDERMANRSPIDERMAN
SPIDERMANESPIDERMAN
SPIDERMANSPIDERMANA
SPIDERMANTSPIDERMAN
ESPIDERMANRSPIDERMAN
SPIDERMANGSPIDERMAN
SPIDERMANOSPIDERMANO
SPIDERMANDSPIDERMAN

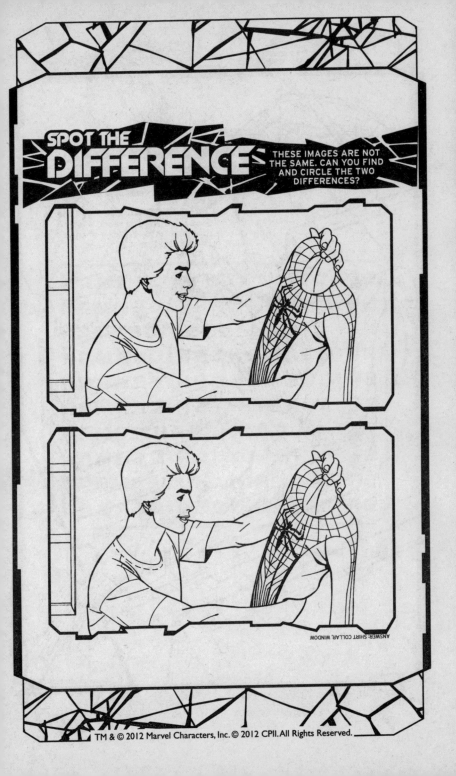

DRAW SPIDER-MAN

Using the grid as a guide, draw the picture in the box below.

FINISH THE PICTURE

USING THE EXAMPLE BELOW AS A GUIDE, COMPLETE THE PICTURE OF SPIDER-MAN.

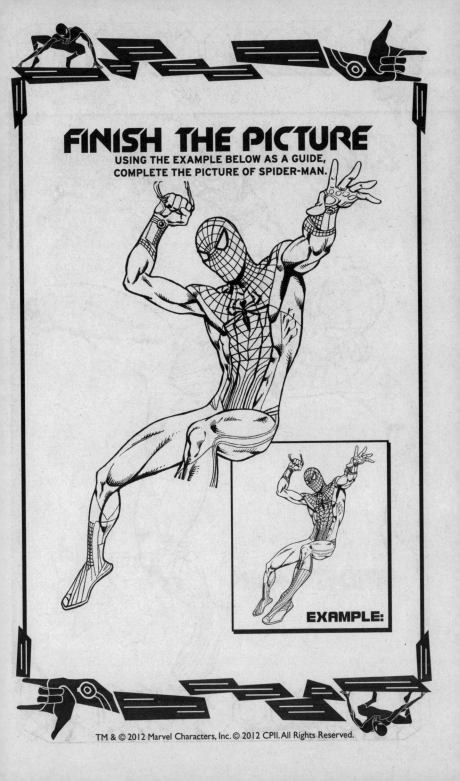

EXAMPLE:

WORD SCRAMBLE

USING THE WORDS FROM THE LIST,
UNSCRAMBLE THE LETTERS TO
CORRECTLY SPELL EACH WORD.

WPORES _____

ESSNES _____

TSERHGNT _____

YGTIAIL _____

EPSED _____

OCURAEG _____

WORD LIST...

AGILITY
STRENGTH
SENSES

SPEED
COURAGE
POWERS

SNAP SHOT

USE THE GRID TO TRANSFER THE SNAP SHOT AND COMPLETE THE PICTURE.

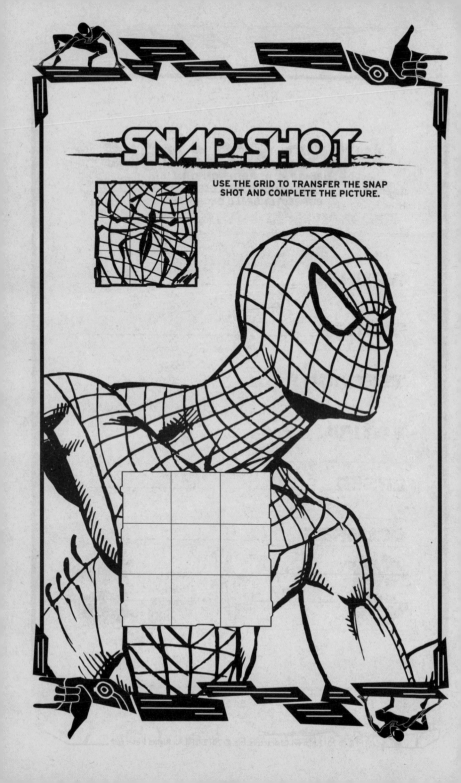

HOW MANY?

HOW MANY WORDS CAN YOU MAKE USING THE LETTERS IN
RICHARD AND MARY PARKER

EXAMPLE: ARACHNID

_____

_____   _____

_____

_____

_____

_____

_____

_____

_____

_____

_____

_____

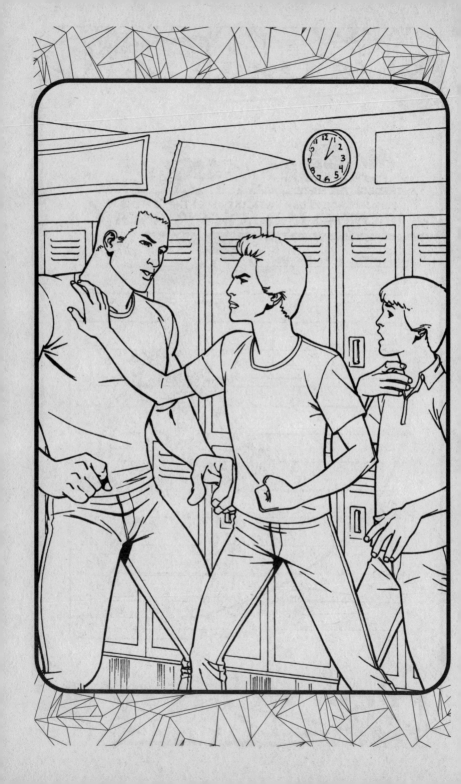

MAZE
FIND YOUR WAY THROUGH THE MAZE!

START

FINISH

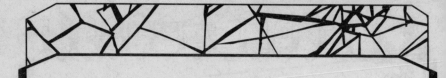

EXAMPLE

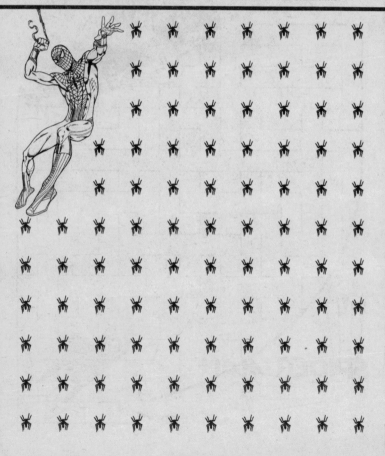

MATCHING

DRAW A LINE TO MATCH THE ITEMS TO THEIR NAMES.

WEB-SHOOTER

SPIDER SYMBOL

SPIDER-MAN

MISSING PIECE

FIND THE MISSING PIECE OF THE IMAGE TO FINISH THE PICTURE!

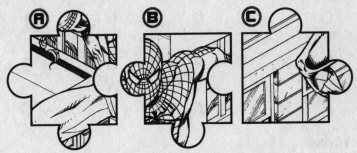

FOLLOW THE PATH

USING THE LETTERS, IN ORDER, FROM THE NAME **OSCORP**,
FOLLOW THE CORRECT PATH TO FIND YOUR WAY THROUGH THE MAZE.

START

C	S	O	T	C	S	O	N
O	A	P	R	O	F	H	Z
R	P	T	N	S	G	U	A
R	O	S	C	O	R	B	R
N	V	P	U	G	P	O	D
O	C	S	O	K	N	S	I
R	X	D	P	R	O	C	S
P	R	I	A	N	S	I	Q

FINISH

TIC-TAC-TOE

USE THESE TIC-TAC-TOE GRIDS TO CHALLENGE YOUR FAMILY AND FRIENDS!

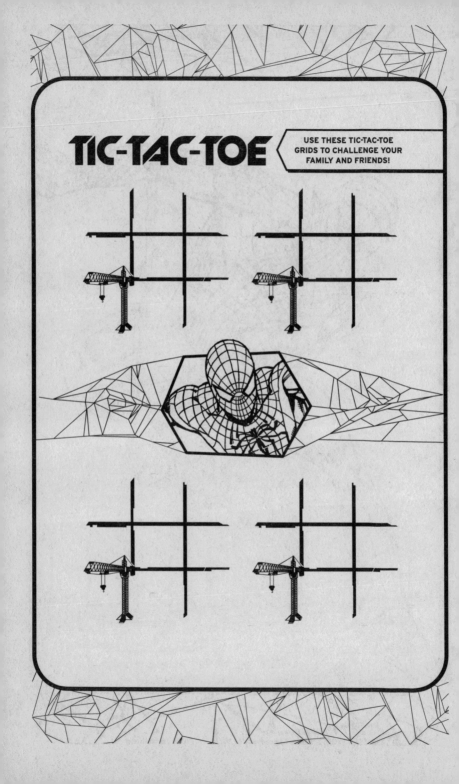

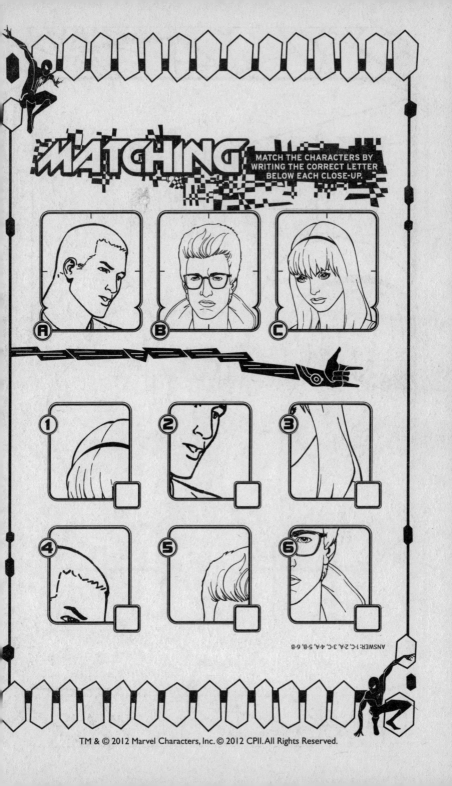

MATCHING

MATCH THE CHARACTERS BY WRITING THE CORRECT LETTER BELOW EACH CLOSE-UP.

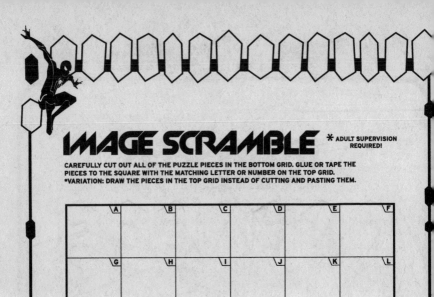

IMAGE SCRAMBLE

* ADULT SUPERVISION REQUIRED!

CAREFULLY CUT OUT ALL OF THE PUZZLE PIECES IN THE BOTTOM GRID. GLUE OR TAPE THE
PIECES TO THE SQUARE WITH THE MATCHING LETTER OR NUMBER ON THE TOP GRID.
*VARIATION: DRAW THE PIECES IN THE TOP GRID INSTEAD OF CUTTING AND PASTING THEM.

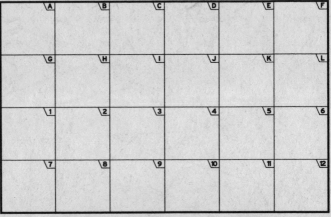

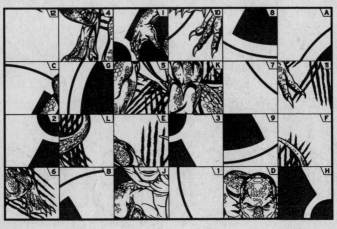

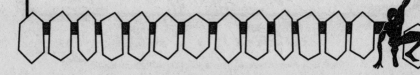

TRANSFER

USING THE PATHS, TRANSFER THE LETTERS
INTO THE BOXES TO UNSCRAMBLE THE WORD.

C N E I E C S

WORD SEARCH

Find and circle the words in the puzzle below.

- POLICE
- CAPTAIN
- VIGILANTE
- ARREST
- PURSUE
- ENEMY

```
E F L B S V W E N A N Y J
C R D Q M I H C L P M F R
S J D V T P L T L O E H B
K O I M H H F J Z L D Q Y
T V K V Y G L R N I U X O
W C I P A B U Z V C Y X N
D A M G Q G P Z U E N G A
F P P Y I T C N B I X Y R
T T C U L L I E C V M X R
P A D P R J A F G E J P E
V I L B X S U N N R F H S
S N W W X I U E T S S X T
Q X Q X X U D E H E P A U
N B E Y U P T G B Y E F L
B Y C M U X V X R N C K O
```

CRACK THE CODE

USING THE SECRET CODE BELOW, FILL IN THE BLANKS
AND REVEAL THE HIDDEN WORDS!

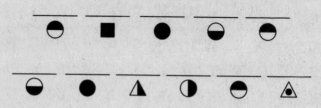

A	B	C	D	E	F	G	H	I
●	○	◉	◐	◑	◉	◑	◐	⊗

J	K	L	M	N	O	P	Q	R
★	★	▽	△	◢	▼	▷	◁	◬

S	T	U	V	W	X	Y	Z
▲	▼	□	■	◧	▣	▬	▭

SECRET MESSAGE

Cross out the word ARACHNID every time you see it in the box. When you reach a letter that does not belong, write it in the shapes below to reveal the secret message.

```
A R A C H N I D A R A C H N I D
A R A C H N I D W A R A C H N I D
A R A C H N I D A R A C H N I D E
A R A C H N I D B A R A C H N I D
S A R A C H N I D A R A C H N I D
A R A C H N I D A R A C H N I D L
A R A C H N I D I A R A C H N I D
N A R A C H N I D G A R A C H N I D
A R A C H N I D A R A C H N I D
E A R A C H N I D R A R A C H N I D
```

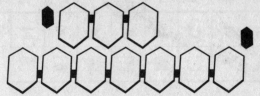

SPOT THE DIFFERENCE

THESE IMAGES ARE NOT THE SAME. CAN YOU FIND AND CIRCLE THE TWO DIFFERENCES?

ANSWER: WEB-SHOOTER, WINDOW

DRAW GWEN STACY

Using the grid as a guide, draw the picture in the box below.

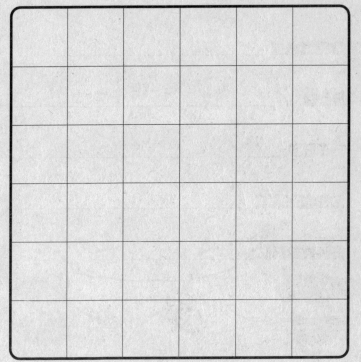

WORD SCRAMBLE

USING THE WORDS FROM THE LIST, UNSCRAMBLE THE LETTERS TO CORRECTLY SPELL EACH WORD.

CHMTISRYE _____

OOBKS _____

ALB _____

STET _____

SINEECC _____

EKABRE _____

WORD LIST...

BEAKER
BOOKS
TEST

LAB
SCIENCE
CHEMISTRY

SNAP SHOT

USE THE GRID TO TRANSFER THE SNAP
SHOT AND COMPLETE THE PICTURE.

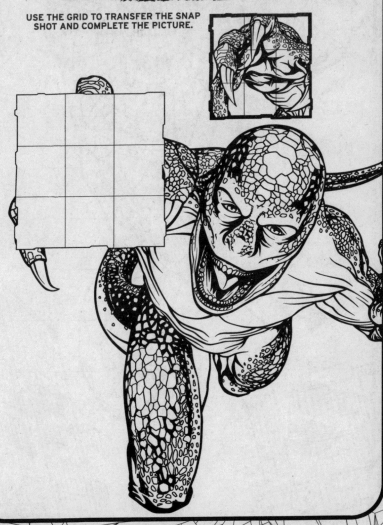

FINISH THE PICTURE

**USING THE EXAMPLE BELOW AS A GUIDE,
COMPLETE THE PICTURE OF SPIDEY.**

EXAMPLE:

MAZE

THERE IS ONLY ONE WAY OUT! SEE IF YOU CAN FIND YOUR WAY
THROUGH THE MAZE WITHOUT RUNNING INTO DR. CONNORS.

START

FINISH

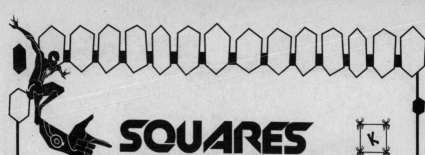

SQUARES

TAKING TURNS, CONNECT A LINE FROM ONE SPIDER TO ANOTHER. WHOEVER
MAKES THE LINE THAT COMPLETES THE BOX PUTS THEIR INITIALS INSIDE THAT
BOX. THE PERSON WITH THE MOST SQUARES AT THE END OF THE GAME WINS!

HOW MANY?

HOW MANY WORDS CAN YOU MAKE USING THE LETTERS IN
HORRIFIC TRANSFORMATION

EXAMPLE: TOMATO

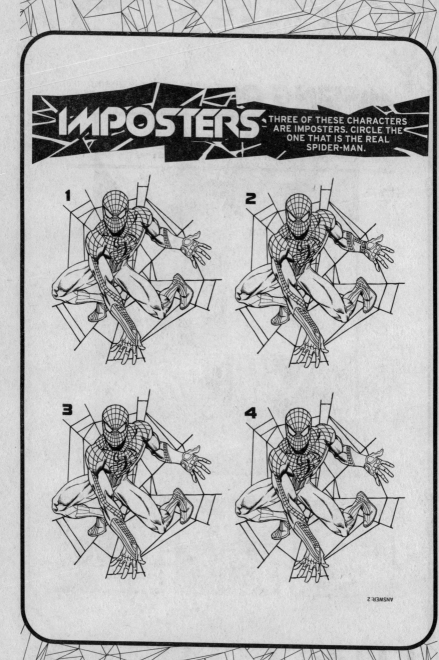

IMPOSTERS

THREE OF THESE CHARACTERS ARE IMPOSTERS. CIRCLE THE ONE THAT IS THE REAL SPIDER-MAN.

FOLLOW THE PATH

USING THE LETTERS, IN ORDER, FROM THE WORD **INJECTION**,
FOLLOW THE CORRECT PATH TO FIND YOUR WAY THROUGH THE MAZE.

START

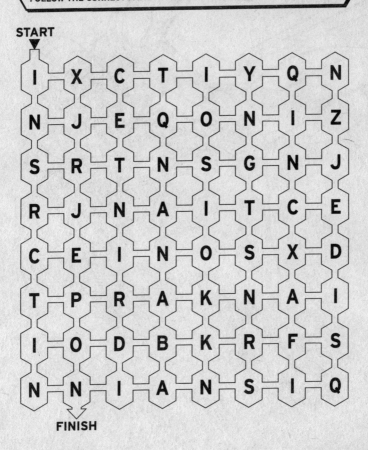

FINISH

TIC-TAC-TOE

USE THESE TIC-TAC-TOE GRIDS TO CHALLENGE YOUR FAMILY AND FRIENDS!

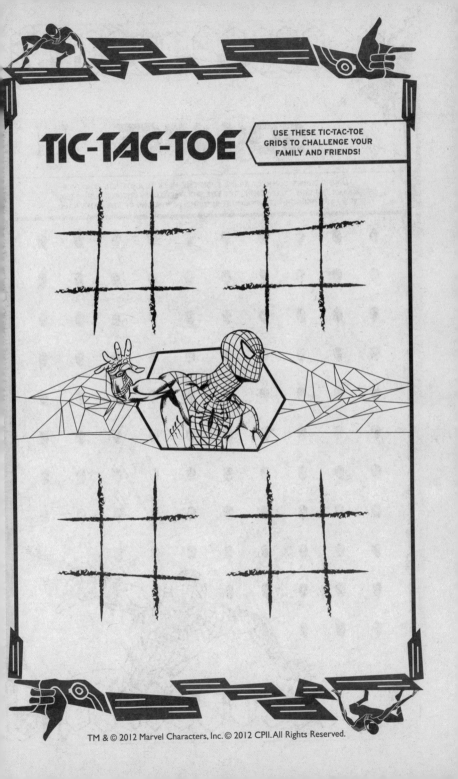

SQUARES

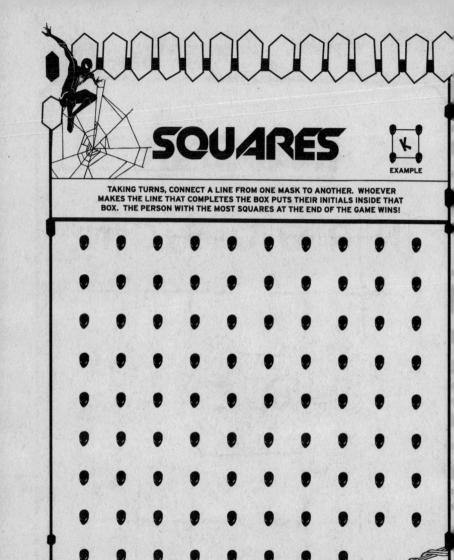

EXAMPLE

TAKING TURNS, CONNECT A LINE FROM ONE MASK TO ANOTHER. WHOEVER
MAKES THE LINE THAT COMPLETES THE BOX PUTS THEIR INITIALS INSIDE THAT
BOX. THE PERSON WITH THE MOST SQUARES AT THE END OF THE GAME WINS!

TRANSFER

USING THE PATHS, TRANSFER THE LETTERS
INTO THE BOXES TO UNSCRAMBLE THE WORD.

N R O O S C N

ANSWER: CONNORS

IMAGE SCRAMBLE

CAREFULLY CUT OUT ALL OF THE PUZZLE PIECES IN THE BOTTOM GRID. GLUE OR TAPE THE PIECES TO THE SQUARE WITH THE MATCHING LETTER OR NUMBER ON THE TOP GRID.
*VARIATION: DRAW THE PIECES IN THE TOP GRID INSTEAD OF CUTTING AND PASTING THEM.

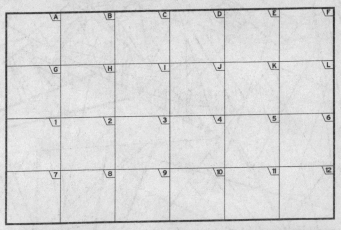

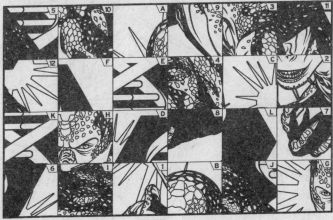

WORD SEARCH

Find and circle the words in the puzzle below.

- ACCIDENT
- ANTIDOTE
- FORMULA
- INJECTION
- MUTATE
- SERUM

```
C K L B X B Q Z W O B X F
I I I X M A M M S E R U M
X A L R V A X C G R D X Y
T N Q I V T C R R S R Y X
K T A I N J E C T I O N W
U I K F E R C W I Y U C X
J D Y U E G L H I D S R Q
R O C J E C I R C U E W Q
T T T M R Y X F V Q S N V
M E J U N U T O W J S Z T
P Y B T P Q C R T N X H Z
B H O A B O S M K F I Z T
H A B T L Y A U A E J Q E
I N M E C Z V L A N I A A
I F M Z N Y B A V R W H Y
```

SPOT THE DIFFERENCE

THESE IMAGES ARE NOT THE SAME. CAN YOU FIND AND CIRCLE THE TWO DIFFERENCES?

ANSWER: GLASSES, DESK

CRACK THE CODE

USING THE SECRET CODE BELOW, FILL IN THE BLANKS AND REVEAL THE HIDDEN WORDS!

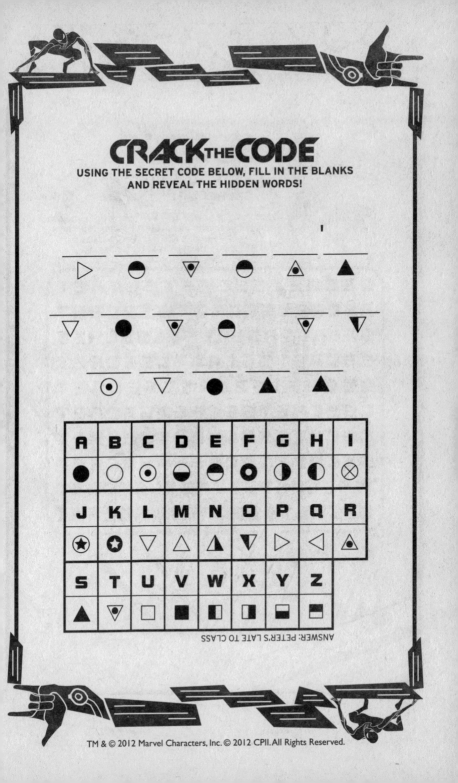

A	B	C	D	E	F	G	H	I
●	○	◉	◐	◑	◓	◗	◖	⊗

J	K	L	M	N	O	P	Q	R
★	✪	▽	△	◤	▼	▷	◁	◬

S	T	U	V	W	X	Y	Z
▲	▼	□	■	◨	◧	▬	▭

SECRET MESSAGE

Cross out the word **SECRET** every time you see it in the box. When you reach a letter that does not belong, write it in the shapes below to reveal the secret message.

```
SECRETSECRETSECRET
SECRETSECRETWSECRET
SECRETASECRETLSECRET
SECRETSECRETLSECRET
SECRETSECRETSECRET
CSECRETSECRETSECRET
SECRETRSECRETSECRET
SECRETSECRETASECRET
WSECRETSECRETLSECRET
SECRETESECRETRSECRET
```

IMPOSTERS — THREE OF THESE CHARACTERS ARE IMPOSTERS. CIRCLE THE ONE THAT IS THE REAL SPIDER-MAN.

1

2

3

4

ANSWER: 3

DRAW SPIDER-MAN

Using the grid as a guide, draw the picture in the box below.

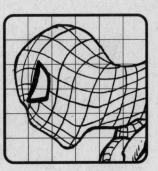

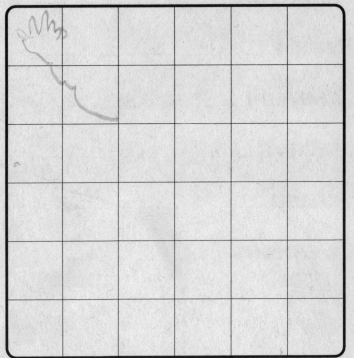

WORD SCRAMBLE

USING THE WORDS FROM THE LIST,
UNSCRAMBLE THE LETTERS TO
CORRECTLY SPELL EACH WORD.

RPENTSA_____

YRAM_____

CHDRARI_____

SHNIVA_____

CLESU_____

WERNSAS_____

WORD LIST...

ANSWERS
MARY
RICHARD

VANISH
CLUES
PARENTS

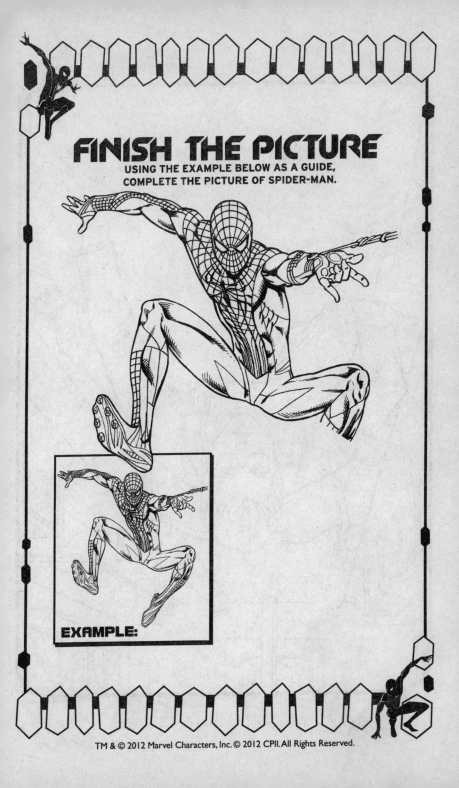

FINISH THE PICTURE

**USING THE EXAMPLE BELOW AS A GUIDE,
COMPLETE THE PICTURE OF SPIDER-MAN.**

EXAMPLE:

GWEN LOST

GWEN STACY NEEDS YOUR HELP!
CAN YOU FIND YOUR WAY TO THE CENTER OF THE MAZE?

START

SNAP-SHOT

USE THE GRID TO TRANSFER THE SNAP SHOT AND COMPLETE THE PICTURE.

HOW MANY?

HOW MANY WORDS CAN YOU MAKE USING THE LETTERS IN

RADIOACTIVE SPIDER BITE

EXAMPLE: RIPTIDE

_____   _____
_____   _____
_____   _____
_____   _____
_____   _____
_____   _____
_____   _____
_____   _____
                               _____
                               _____
                               _____

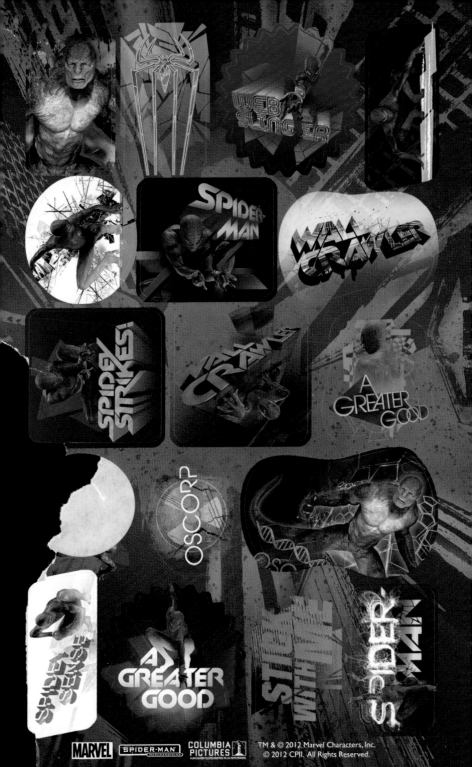

MISSING PIECE

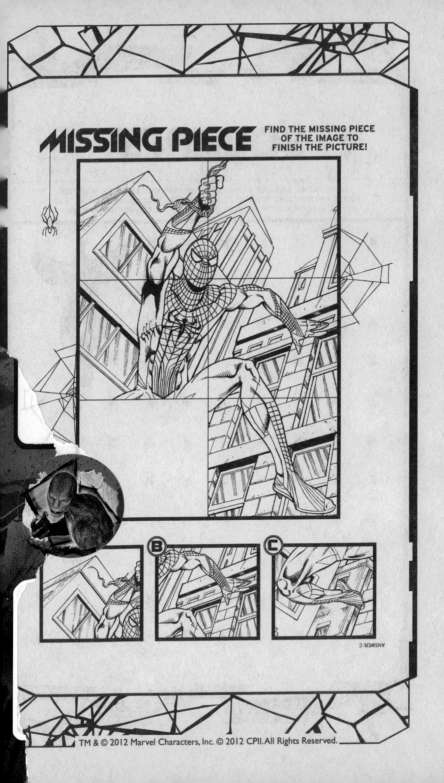

ANSWER: C

SQUARES

EXAMPLE

TAKING TURNS, CONNECT A LINE FROM ONE SPIDER TO ANOTHER. WHOEVER
MAKES THE LINE THAT COMPLETES THE BOX PUTS THEIR INITIALS INSIDE THAT
BOX. THE PERSON WITH THE MOST SQUARES AT THE END OF THE GAME WINS!

MATCHING

DRAW A LINE TO MATCH THE CHARACTERS TO THEIR SILHOUETTES.

FOLLOW THE PATH

USING THE LETTERS, IN ORDER, FROM THE WORD **VIGILANTE**,
FOLLOW THE CORRECT PATH TO FIND YOUR WAY THROUGH THE MAZE.

START ▼

A	L	I	V	G	Y	Q	N
N	A	G	I	P	E	V	I
T	R	T	N	N	T	U	G
E	V	I	A	A	P	L	I
N	V	G	I	L	N	A	D
K	P	I	V	E	T	A	I
G	X	G	I	L	A	N	T
N	R	I	A	N	S	I	E

FINISH ↓

TRANSFER

**USING THE PATHS, TRANSFER THE LETTERS
INTO THE BOXES TO UNSCRAMBLE THE WORD.**

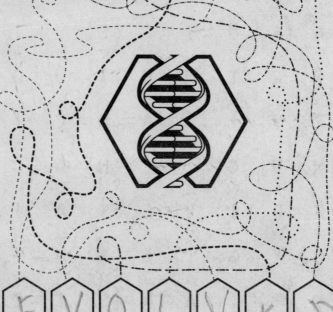

V D O E E V L

E V O L V E D

IMAGE SCRAMBLE

* ADULT SUPERVISION REQUIRED!

CAREFULLY CUT OUT ALL OF THE PUZZLE PIECES IN THE BOTTOM GRID. GLUE OR TAPE THE PIECES TO THE SQUARE WITH THE MATCHING LETTER OR NUMBER ON THE TOP GRID.
*VARIATION: DRAW THE PIECES IN THE TOP GRID INSTEAD OF CUTTING AND PASTING THEM.

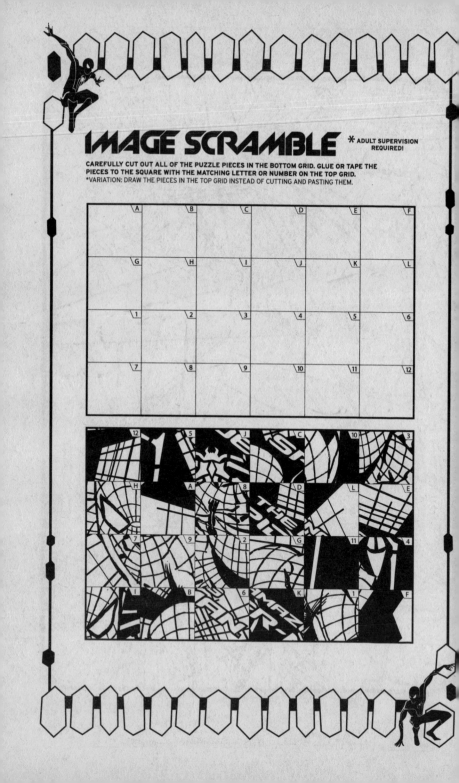

WORD SEARCH

Find and circle the words in the puzzle below.

- DANGER
- EVADE
- ENCOUNTER
- FLEE
- CONFRONT
- HIDEOUT

```
A X B M G F J M K O Z M J
U J O V I B F J H P U N Z
J V A R R C R E D H X U X
J G J U I P Y N U G D H C
A O A L K G A C P K N V L
R F X N C D A O I Q F C E
F S H M O O A U A O G E C
F M J E N Y F N K Y L H T
P U N O F S V T G F W U Y
I N Q P R X R E C E O O O
V J Y G O B X R V E R L O
N G L T N V P H D A E Z C
I P B V T N L I V U D J D
P M T T N D H E T E B E S
V T M K Z U H H R Z T N M
```

TIC-TAC-TOE

CRACK THE CODE

USING THE SECRET CODE BELOW, FILL IN THE BLANKS AND REVEAL THE HIDDEN WORDS!

A	B	C	D	E	F	G	H	I
●	○	◉	◓	◒	◎	◑	◖◗	⊗

J	K	L	M	N	O	P	Q	R
★	☆	▽	△	◣	▼	▷	◁	◬

S	T	U	V	W	X	Y	Z
▲	▼	□	■	▮	▯	▭	▬

SECRET MESSAGE

Cross out the word **POWER** every time you see it in the box. When you reach a letter that does not belong, write it in the shapes below to reveal the secret message.

```
P O W E R P O W E R P O W E R
P O W E R S P O W E R P O W E R
T P O W E R I P O W E R P O W E R
P O W E R C P O W E R P O W E R
P O W E R P O W E R K P O W E R
P O W E R P O W E R P O W E R W
P O W E R I P O W E R T P O W E R
P O W E R P O W E R H P O W E R
P O W E R P O W E R P O W E R
P O W E R M P O W E R E P O W E R
```

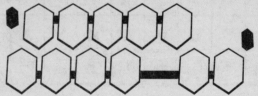

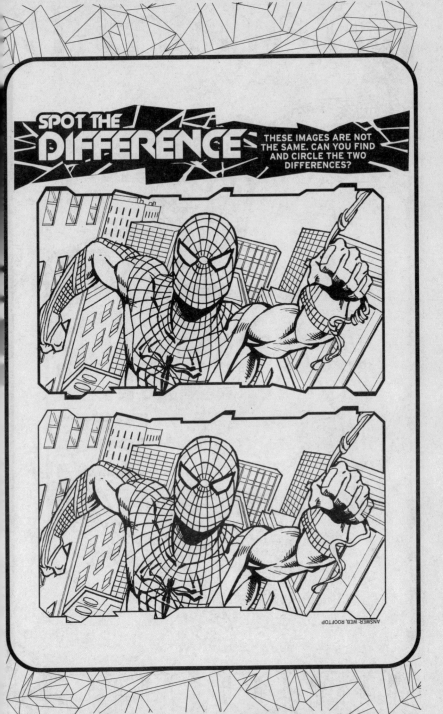

DRAW
THE SPIDER
SYMBOL

Using the grid as a guide, draw the picture in the box below.

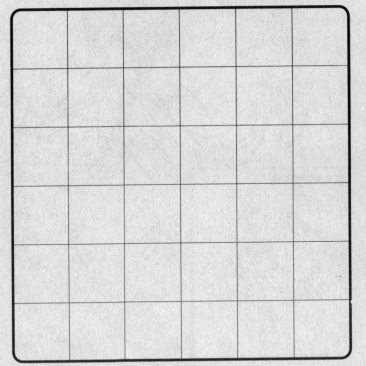

FINISH THE PICTURE

USING THE EXAMPLE BELOW AS A GUIDE,
COMPLETE THE PICTURE OF SPIDER-MAN.

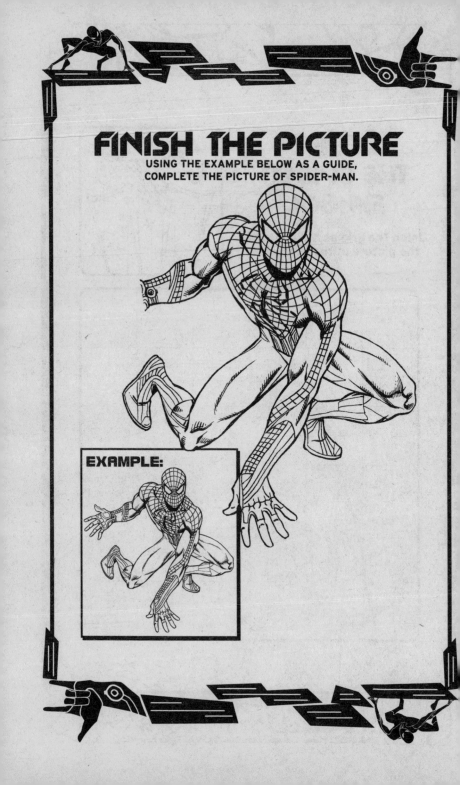

EXAMPLE:

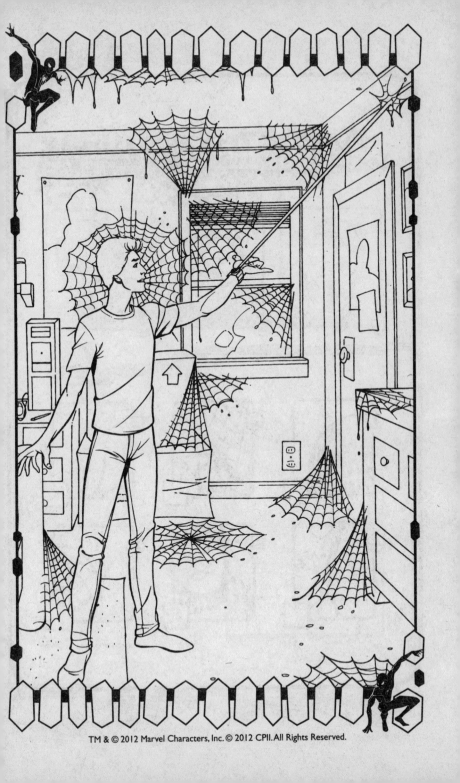

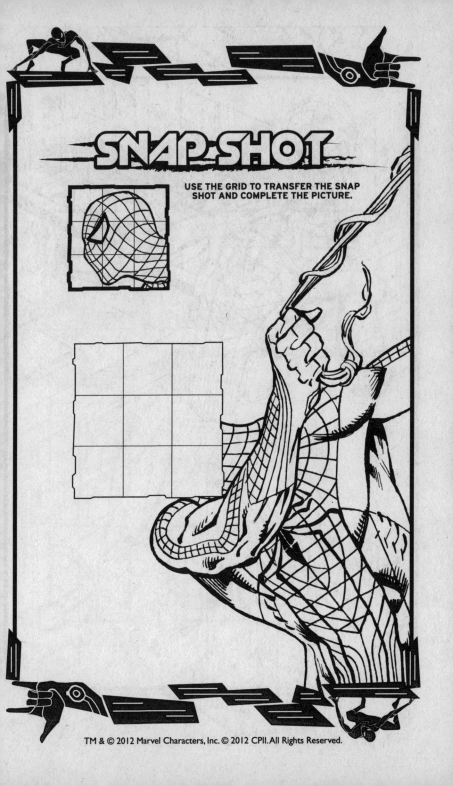

SNAP·SHOT

USE THE GRID TO TRANSFER THE SNAP SHOT AND COMPLETE THE PICTURE.

WORD SCRAMBLE

USING THE WORDS FROM THE LIST,
UNSCRAMBLE THE LETTERS TO
CORRECTLY SPELL EACH WORD.

OOTCDR _____

NNOOCRS _____

TLARE-GEO _____

CIACNTED _____

REINFD _____

TRAPNER _____

WORD LIST...

DOCTOR
FRIEND
ALTER-EGO

ACCIDENT
CONNORS
PARTNER

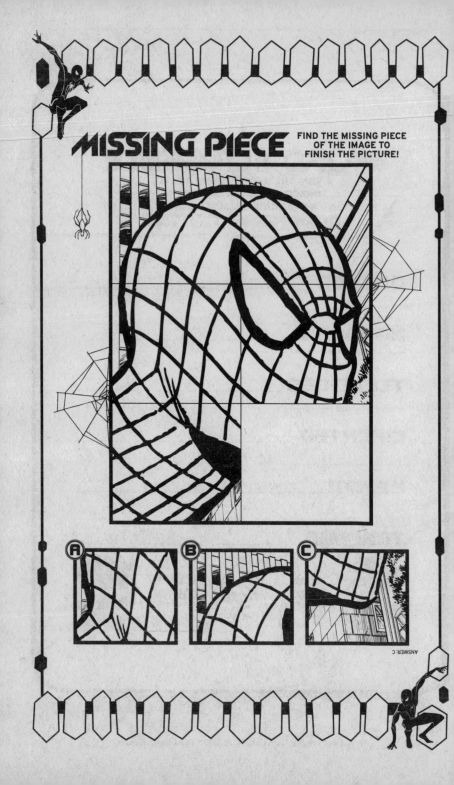

MISSING PIECE

FIND THE MISSING PIECE OF THE IMAGE TO FINISH THE PICTURE!

A

B

C

ANSWER: C

HOW MANY?

HOW MANY WORDS CAN YOU MAKE USING THE LETTERS IN
RAMPAGING REPTILE

EXAMPLE: PIER

CONFUTATION

HELP SPIDER-MAN MAKE HIS WAY TO HELP DR. CONNORS!

start

finish

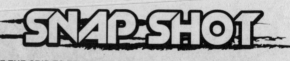

SNAP·SHOT

USE THE GRID TO TRANSFER THE SNAP SHOT AND COMPLETE THE PICTURE.

MATCHING

DRAW A LINE TO MATCH THE CHARACTERS TO THEIR SILHOUETTES.

SQUARES

EXAMPLE

TAKING TURNS, CONNECT A LINE FROM ONE MASK TO ANOTHER. WHOEVER
MAKES THE LINE THAT COMPLETES THE BOX PUTS THEIR INITIALS INSIDE THAT
BOX. THE PERSON WITH THE MOST SQUARES AT THE END OF THE GAME WINS!

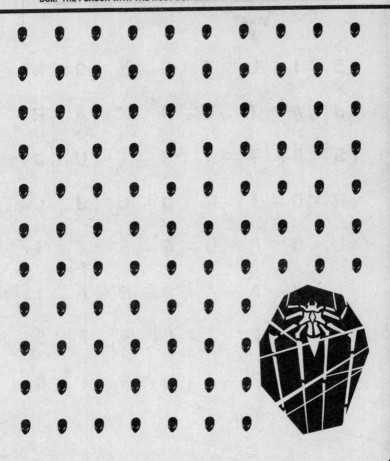

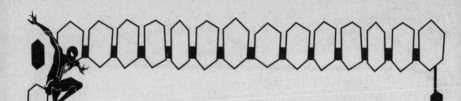

FOLLOW THE PATH

USING THE LETTERS, IN ORDER, FROM THE WORD **LIZARD**,
FOLLOW THE CORRECT PATH TO FIND YOUR WAY THROUGH THE MAZE.

START

B	I	L	T	G	Y	Q	N
J	A	I	Z	P	Z	A	R
S	R	T	A	S	I	U	D
R	D	I	R	D	L	B	L
L	D	R	U	G	S	Z	I
I	P	A	A	D	R	A	I
Z	A	Z	I	L	R	F	S
N	R	D	A	N	S	I	Q

FINISH

TRANSFER

USING THE PATHS, TRANSFER THE LETTERS INTO THE BOXES TO UNSCRAMBLE THE WORD.

A L L I I V N

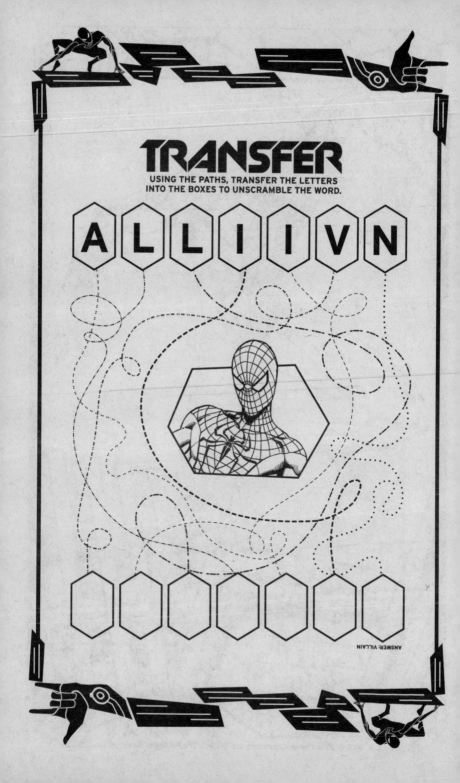

IMAGE SCRAMBLE

* ADULT SUPERVISION REQUIRED!

CAREFULLY CUT OUT ALL OF THE PUZZLE PIECES IN THE BOTTOM GRID. GLUE OR TAPE THE
PIECES TO THE SQUARE WITH THE MATCHING LETTER OR NUMBER ON THE TOP GRID.
*VARIATION: DRAW THE PIECES IN THE TOP GRID INSTEAD OF CUTTING AND PASTING THEM.

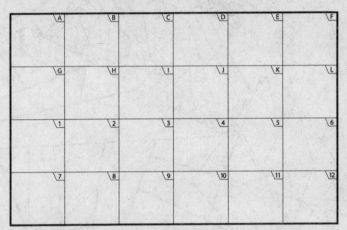

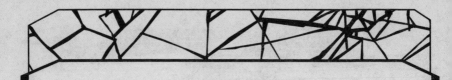

WORD SEARCH

Find and circle the words in the puzzle below.

- EXPERIMENT
- SECRET
- UNDERGROUND
- LIZARD
- SEWERS
- VILLAIN

```
Q I L M L P L I Z A R D J
K G T S N L V N J Q S G M
S H X O P X W O F U E A G
W E J E Y L T P G M U X E
X U W X Q A C E N G U F I
S I O E M Q T X U B N X A
Y F O D R V B P B F D L R
I S W T D S E J S E Q D
S M E O X T C R B V R R L
W W K C T A C I J I G F Q
R A R E R Q A M Q L R O X
D M V K Y E V E G L O W R
F F M B B P T N H A U W C
Z I B E V T X T N I N N B
Q J H H Y M A J G N D E P
```

TIC-TAC-TOE

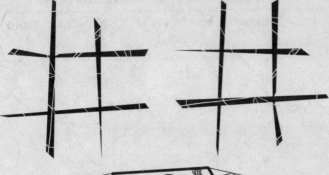

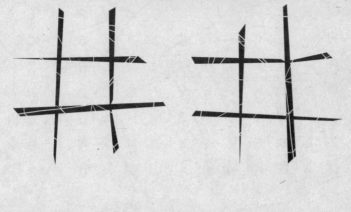

CRACK THE CODE

USING THE SECRET CODE BELOW, FILL IN THE BLANKS AND REVEAL THE HIDDEN WORDS!

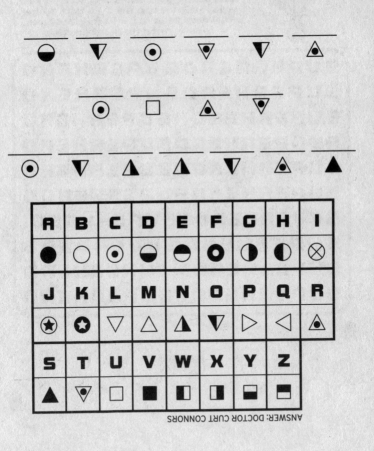

SECRET MESSAGE

Cross out the word **SUPERHERO** every time you see it in the box. When you reach a letter that does not belong, write it in the shapes below to reveal the secret message.

SUPERHEROSUPERHERO
SUPERHEROSUPERHERO
SUPERHEROHSUPERHERO
ASUPERHEROSUPERHERO
SUPERHERONSUPERHERO
SUPERHEROSUPERHEROG
SUPERHEROTSUPERHEROI
SUPERHEROSUPERHERO
SUPERHEROMSUPERHERO
SUPERHEROESUPERHERO

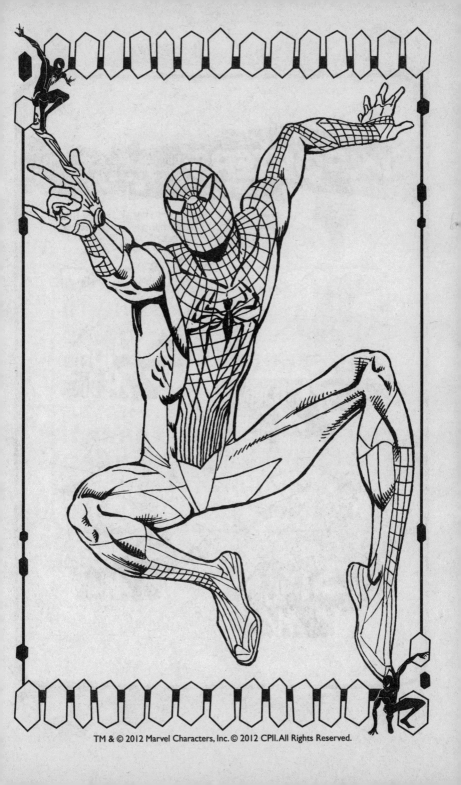

IMPOSTERS

THREE OF THESE CHARACTERS ARE IMPOSTERS. CIRCLE THE ONE THAT IS THE REAL SPIDER-MAN.

ANSWER: 4

WORD SCRAMBLE

**USING THE WORDS FROM THE LIST,
UNSCRAMBLE THE LETTERS TO
CORRECTLY SPELL EACH WORD.**

DSPERI _____

RIDOAATCEIV _____

CWARL _____

TIEB _____

MONEV _____

OPSOIN _____

WORD LIST...

BITE
RADIOACTIVE
CRAWL

SPIDER
VENOM
POISON

DRAW
SPIDER-MAN

Using the grid as a guide, draw the picture in the box below.

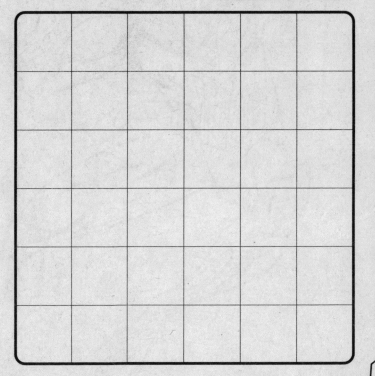

SQUARES

TAKING TURNS, CONNECT A LINE FROM ONE SPIDER TO ANOTHER. WHOEVER MAKES THE LINE THAT COMPLETES THE BOX PUTS THEIR INITIALS INSIDE THAT BOX. THE PERSON WITH THE MOST SQUARES AT THE END OF THE GAME WINS!

MATCHING

DRAW A LINE TO MATCH
THE CHARACTERS TO
THEIR SILHOUETTES.

FINISH THE PICTURE

**USING THE EXAMPLE BELOW AS A GUIDE,
COMPLETE THE PICTURE OF SPIDER-MAN.**

EXAMPLE:

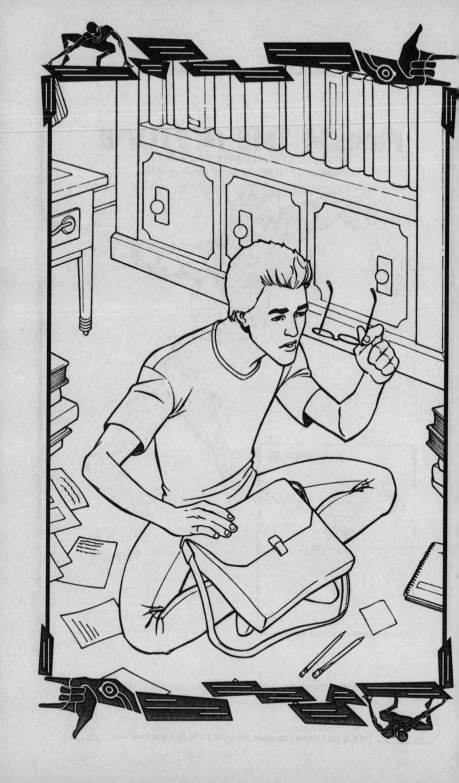

MISSING PIECE

FIND THE MISSING PIECE OF THE IMAGE TO FINISH THE PICTURE!

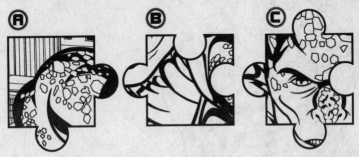

A B C

ANSWER: B

SNAP·SHOT

USE THE GRID TO TRANSFER THE SNAP SHOT AND COMPLETE THE PICTURE.

HOW MANY?

HOW MANY WORDS CAN YOU MAKE USING THE LETTERS IN
EVOLUTIONARY STEP

EXAMPLE: PEST

WEB MAZE

HELP SPIDER-MAN FIND HIS WAY OUT!

start

finish

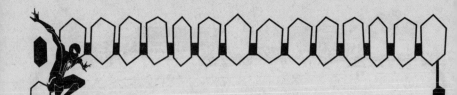

FOLLOW THE PATH

USING THE LETTERS, IN ORDER, FROM THE NAME **NEW YORK**, FOLLOW THE CORRECT PATH TO FIND YOUR WAY THROUGH THE MAZE.

START

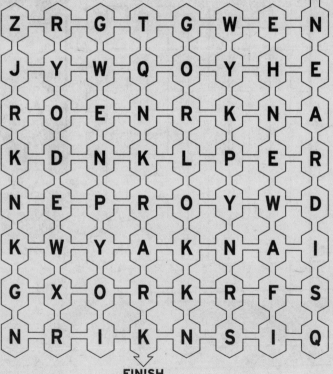

FINISH

MATCHING

DRAW A LINE TO MATCH THE CHARACTERS TO THEIR NAMES.

GWEN STACY

SPIDER-MAN

FLASH THOMPSON

TRANSFER

USING THE PATHS, TRANSFER THE LETTERS INTO THE BOXES TO UNSCRAMBLE THE WORD.

T I I A Y G L

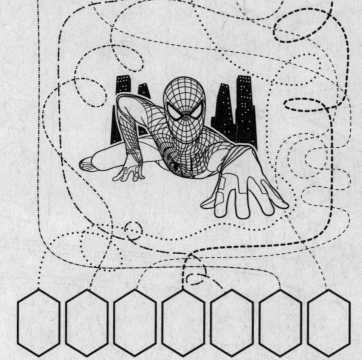

ANSWER: AGILITY

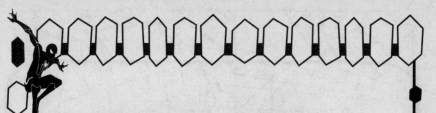

IMAGE SCRAMBLE

CAREFULLY CUT OUT ALL OF THE PUZZLE PIECES IN THE BOTTOM GRID. GLUE OR TAPE THE PIECES TO THE SQUARE WITH THE MATCHING LETTER OR NUMBER ON THE TOP GRID.
*VARIATION: DRAW THE PIECES IN THE TOP GRID INSTEAD OF CUTTING AND PASTING THEM.

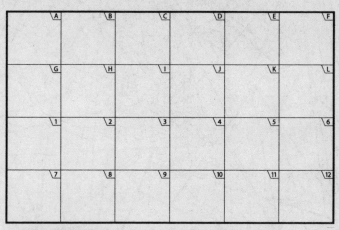

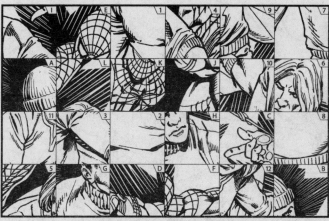

WORD SEARCH

Find and circle the words in the puzzle below.

- CONSTRUCTION
- PEDESTRIANS
- STREETS
- NEW YORK
- SKYSCRAPER
- TRAFFIC

```
R J S D Y K C V J X B S T
J Z S K Y S C R A P E R T
B S C Q M J N C V Q C U G
H R O S E N P E T W O I A
U Q N P S F E J W K R Y X
U L S M M G D U T Y C N O
S B T T E B E B Y N O S E
C M R C A A S V U T B R N
S Q U D S O T C Q P V E K
T A C Y V Y R S S Y Z K X
R O T E F Z I Y B A Q J C
E P I E T R A F F I C F T
E O O P J H N X W Q X Z H
T T N F L A S G C M A J A
S W V O J R M E J K P E Q
```

CR4CK THE CODE

USING THE SECRET CODE BELOW, FILL IN THE BLANKS
AND REVEAL THE HIDDEN WORDS!

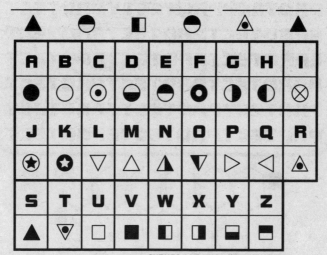

SECRET MESSAGE

Cross out the word **PROTECT** every time you see it in the box. When you reach a letter that does not belong, write it in the shapes below to reveal the secret message.

```
PROTECTPROTECTPROTECTS
PROTECTPPROTECTPROTECT
IPROTECTDPROTECTPROTECT
PROTECTEPROTECTPROTECT
PROTECTPROTECTYPROTECT
SPROTECTPROTECTPROTECT
EPROTECTPROTECTPROTECT
NPROTECTPROTECTPROTECT
PROTECTPROTECTSPROTECT
PROTECTPROTECTEPROTECT
```

THE ESCAPE

HELP SPIDER-MAN FIND HIS WAY TO FREEDOM!

start

finish

Draw
SPIDER-MAN

Using the grid as a guide, draw the picture in the box below.

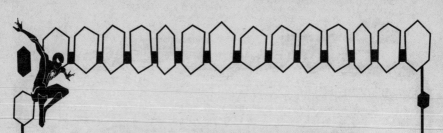

WORD SCRAMBLE

**USING THE WORDS FROM THE LIST,
UNSCRAMBLE THE LETTERS TO
CORRECTLY SPELL EACH WORD.**

SNEW_____

LUBEG_____

THOOPS_____

ROTSY_____

ETIDRO_____

TRWIRE_____

WORD LIST...

STORY
WRITER
PHOTOS

NEWS
EDITOR
BUGLE

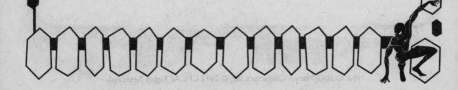

MATCHING

DRAW A LINE TO MATCH THE CHARACTERS TO THEIR SILHOUETTES.

FINISH THE PICTURE

**USING THE EXAMPLE BELOW AS A GUIDE,
COMPLETE THE PICTURE OF PETER PARKER.**

HOW MANY?

HOW MANY WORDS CAN YOU MAKE USING THE LETTERS IN
UNCLE BEN AND AUNT MAY

EXAMPLE: UNBALANCED

_____   _____

_____   _____

_____   _____

_____   _____

_____   _____

_____   _____

_____   _____

_____   _____